S0-AQI-373

NASHA SH
6717 85th Av
BROOKLYN
MN 5544
(763) 496-5

NASHA
SHKOLI

| Grade 2 | Skills 1 |

The Cat Bandit

Reader

Amplify Core Knowledge Language Arts | Core Knowledge

ISBN 978-1-61700-207-6

© 2015 The Core Knowledge Foundation and its licensors
www.coreknowledge.org

All Rights Reserved.

Core Knowledge Language Arts is a trademark
of the Core Knowledge Foundation.

Trademarks and trade names are shown in this book strictly for
illustrative and educational purposes and are the property of their
respective owners. References herein should not be regarded as
affecting the validity of said trademarks and trade names.

Printed in the USA
01 RRCV 2016

The Hot Dog

Mom had a hot dog.

She left the hot dog on a shelf in the den.

The hot dog sent up a smell.

The smell drifted and drifted.

The cat bandit sat on the deck, wishing he had a snack.

Then the hot dog smell hit him.

Such a smell!

Sniff, sniff, sniff!

The cat bandit ran in the den.

He spotted the hot dog up on the shelf.

He got up on a bench.

Then he sprang up on the TV set.

Then, with a big jump, he sprang up and landed on the shelf.

Then—munch, munch, munch—the cat bandit had himself a picnic lunch.

The Chicken Nugget

Hank set his dish in the sink.

He left a big chicken nugget on the dish.

The nugget was still hot.

The smell of chicken drifted up from the sink.

It drifted into the den.

The cat bandit was napping in the den.

But he was sniffing as he slept.

Sniff, sniff, sniff!

The cat bandit sprang up.

He ran in and spotted the nugget in the sink.

He sat a bit, thinking up a plan.

Then he went to the closet and got a bunch of boxes.

He set up a box.

Then he set a big box next to that box.

Then he set the biggest box next to the sink.

The cat bandit set off running.

He ran up the boxes, hopping from box to box.

Then—munch, munch, munch—that was the end of the chicken nugget.

9

The Snack Mix

Beth left a basket of snack mix on a shelf.

The cat bandit spotted the snack mix.

He felt he had to get it.

But how?

He sat thinking.

Then he got up and ran off to the deck.

The cat bandit got the grilling tongs Dad kept next to the gas grill.

He set the tongs up on the rug.

Then he went and got a bunch of rocks.

He set the rocks on the rug.

He got a rock and set it down on the top tong.

He set his leg on the top tong to press it down.

Then he let the tong spring up.

Swish! The rock went zipping off.

Bing! The rock hit the shelf.

But it did not hit the basket with the snack mix.

The bandit set a rock on the tongs and shot it.

Swish, bing!

Swish, bing!

Swish, bing!

The bandit shot six rocks.

But the rocks did not hit the basket of snack mix.

At last—swish, smack!

The seventh rock hit the basket.

The basket fell down.

It landed on the rug.

The rug was dotted with snack mix.

Then—chomp, chomp, chomp—that was the end of the snack mix.

The Ham

Mom left a pink ham sitting in a big black pan.

The cat bandit was resting on a quilt when he got a whiff of the ham.

What was that smell?

It was ham!

Where was the ham?

The cat bandit set off, sniffing as he went.

He went on sniffing until he spotted the ham.

But the ham was up on top.

How was he to get it down?

That was the problem.

The cat bandit ran to the closet and got a belt.

Then he ran to the shed and got a strong magnet.

He stuck the magnet on the end of the belt.

The magnet stuck to the belt.

Then the cat bandit swung the belt.

Clang! The magnet on the end of the belt hit the pan.

It stuck to the pan.

In a flash, the cat bandit was tugging on the belt.

Tug, tug, tug!

Yank, yank, yank!

At last, the pan slid off.

It fell down and landed with a clang.

Then—munch, munch, munch—that was the end of the ham.

The Fish

Once Mom hung a fish up on a string.

The cat bandit was scratching himself when he got a whiff of the fish.

Quick as a flash he ran into the kitchen.

The bandit spotted the fish hanging on the string.

He sat down to think up a plan to get the fish.

The cat bandit ran and got Mom's glasses.

He set the glasses on a bench that was in the sun.

The sun shone on the two lenses of the glasses.

The lenses glinted in the sun.

The bandit slid the glasses a bit to the left.

He slid the glasses until one of the lenses sent hot sun flashing onto the string.

Then he sat.

25

The sun from the glasses shone on the string.

The string got hot.

The wax on the string melted.

Then, rip!

The fish fell.

Then—munch, munch, munch—that was the end of the fish.

The Milk

Once Beth left a glass of milk on the deck.

The cat bandit spotted it.

It was up where he could not get it.

The bandit was sad.

But then he spotted a string that ran from the shed to the deck.

Mom had hung wet socks, wet pants, and a wet jacket on the string.

The bandit grinned.

The cat bandit went and got Dad's belt.

Then he got up on top of the shed.

He swung the belt on top of the string.

Then he held on to the belt and jumped off the shed.

Whiz!

The bandit went zipping off on the string.

Pop, pop, pop!

He knocked the socks off the string.

Pop, pop, pop!

He knocked the pants off the string.

Thwack!

He knocked the jacket off the string.

At last the bandit went zipping past the milk.

As he went past, he kicked the cup with his leg.

The cup fell on the deck with a crash.

The bandit landed on the deck.

Then—lap, lap, lap—that was the end of the milk.

The Chips

Once Mom left a big bag of chips on the top shelf in the kitchen.

"The cat will not get them up there," she said.

But it was not long until the cat bandit was up to his tricks.

He got a log, a plank, and a big rock.

He set the rock on the bench.

He set the log on the rug next to the bench.

He set the plank on top of the log.

Then the bandit sat on one end of the plank.

He slid the rock off the bench.

The rock fell and landed on one end of the plank.

Smack!

The end of the plank where the rock fell went down fast.

But the end of the plank the cat bandit was sitting on popped up, and the cat bandit popped up with it.

Whiz!

The cat bandit went zipping up.

The cat bandit did a flip and landed on top of the shelf.

Slash! The bandit cut a big gash in the bag.

Then—crunch, crunch, crunch—that was the end of the chips.

The Catfish

Dad went fishing and got a big catfish.

He left the catfish in a bucket.

Then he locked the bucket in the shed.

"There!" he said as he clicked the lock shut.

"This lock will stop the cat!"

The tempting smell of fish drifted in the wind.

The cat bandit sensed that there was a fish in the shed.

He went to visit.

The shed was locked up.

But that did not stop him!

He went and got a belt.

He hitched the end of the belt to the lock and tugged on it.

But the lock held and the shed just sat there.

43

The cat bandit went and got a dog.

The cat and the dog tugged on the belt.

But still the shed just sat there.

The cat bandit went and got a pig.

The cat, the dog, and the pig tugged on the belt.

That did it.

The shed tilted to the left.

Wham! The shed fell with a crash.

Then—munch, munch, munch—that was the end of the catfish.

About this Book

This book has been created for use by students learning to read with the Core Knowledge Reading Program. Readability levels are suitable for early readers. The book has also been carefully leveled in terms of its "code load," or the number of spellings used in the stories.

The English writing system is complex. It uses more than 200 spellings to stand for 40-odd sounds. Many sounds can be spelled several different ways, and many spellings can be pronounced several different ways. This book has been designed to make early reading experiences simpler and more productive by using a subset of the available spellings. It uses *only* spellings students have been taught to sound out as part of their phonics lessons, plus a handful of Tricky Words, which have also been deliberately introduced in the lessons. This means the stories will be 100% decodable if they are assigned at the proper time.

As the students move through the program, they learn new spellings and the "code load" in the decodable Readers increases gradually. The code load graphic on this page indicates the number of spellings students are expected to know in order to read the first story of the book and the number of spellings students are expected to know in order to read the final stories in the book. The columns on the opposite page list the specific spellings and Tricky Words students are expected to recognize at the beginning of this Reader. The bullets at the bottom of the opposite page identify spellings, Tricky Words, and other topics that are introduced gradually in the unit this Reader accompanies.

Visit us on the web at www.coreknowledge.org.

Code Knowledge assumed at the beginning of this Reader:

Note: The listing below of assumed code knowledge lists the vowel and consonant sounds and spellings, Tricky Words, and other language conventions that are reviewed in Lessons 1–10 of this unit before students begin reading the first story in this Reader.

VOWEL SOUNDS AND SPELLINGS:

/i/ as in s_i_t

/e/ as in b_e_d

/a/ as in h_a_t

/u/ as in b_u_t

/o/ as in h_o_t

CONSONANT SOUNDS AND SPELLINGS:

/p/ as in _p_ot, pe_pp_er

/b/ as in _b_at, ru_bb_ing

/t/ as in _t_op, mi_tt_

/d/ as in _d_og, sle_dd_ing

/k/ as in _c_at, _k_id, so_cc_er, ba_ck_

/g/ as in _g_et, bi_gg_er

/ch/ as in _ch_op

/j/ as in _j_et

/f/ as in _f_at, sni_ff_

/v/ as in _v_et

/s/ as in _s_it, mi_ss_

/z/ as in _z_ip, bu_zz_

/th/ as in _th_in

/th/ as in _th_em

/m/ as in _m_an, swi_mm_ing

/n/ as in _n_ot, ba_nn_er

/ng/ as in so_ng_

/h/ as in _h_ot

/w/ as in _w_et

/l/ as in _l_ip, fi_ll_

/r/ as in _r_ed, fe_rr_et

/y/ as in _y_es

/sh/ as in _sh_ip

/x/ as in ta_x_

OTHER:

• Two-syllable words with short vowels

Code Knowledge added gradually in the unit for this Reader:

Note: The code knowledge and Tricky Words listed below as being added gradually in this unit for this Reader have already been taught in Grade 1 CKLA. However, the specific code knowledge and Tricky Words noted are re-introduced and reviewed in the following stories, as well as in other instructional activities in this unit.

• Beginning with "The Hot Dog": double-letter spellings for consonant sounds, such as /k/ as in clo_ck_, /l/ as in she_ll_, /f/ as in o_ff_, etc.; Tricky Words _he, she, the, a_

• Beginning with "The Chicken Nugget": double-letter spellings for consonant sounds, such as /p/ as in na_pp_ing, /n/ as in ru_nn_ing, /t/ as in spo_tt_ed, etc.; Tricky Words _was, of, from, to_

• Beginning with "The Snack Mix": Tricky Words _down, how_

• Beginning with "The Ham": /qu/ as in _qu_ilt; Tricky Words _what, where_

• Beginning with "The Fish": /w/ as in _wh_iff, /ch/ as in scra_tch_; Tricky Words _once, one, two_

• Beginning with "The Milk": /n/ as _kn_ock, Tricky Word _could_

• Beginning with "The Chips": Tricky Words _there, said_

Core Knowledge Language Arts

Series Editor-in-Chief

E. D. Hirsch, Jr.

President

Linda Bevilacqua

Rights Manager

Elizabeth Bland

Editorial Staff

Mick Anderson
Robin Blackshire
Laura Drummond
Emma Earnst
Lucinda Ewing
Sara Hunt
Rosie McCormick
Cynthia Peng
Liz Pettit
Tonya Ronayne
Deborah Samley
Kate Stephenson
Elizabeth Wafler
James Walsh
Sarah Zelinke

Design and Graphics Staff

Kelsie Harman
Liz Loewenstein
Bridget Moriarty
Lauren Pack
Cecilia Sorochin

Consulting Project Management Services

ScribeConcepts.com

Additional Consulting Services

Erin Kist
Carolyn Pinkerton
Scott Ritchie
Kelina Summers

Acknowledgments

These materials are the result of the work, advice, and encouragement of numerous individuals over many years. Some of those singled out here already know the depth of our gratitude; others may be surprised to find themselves thanked publicly for help they gave quietly and generously for the sake of the enterprise alone. To helpers named and unnamed we are deeply grateful.

Contributors to Earlier Versions of these Materials

Susan B. Albaugh, Kazuko Ashizawa, Kim Berrall, Ang Blanchette, Nancy Braier, Maggie Buchanan, Paula Coyner, Kathryn M. Cummings, Michelle De Groot, Michael Donegan, Diana Espinal, Mary E. Forbes, Michael L. Ford, Sue Fulton, Carolyn Gosse, Dorrit Green, Liza Greene, Ted Hirsch, Danielle Knecht, James K. Lee, Matt Leech, Diane Henry Leipzig, Robin Luecke, Martha G. Mack, Liana Mahoney, Isabel McLean, Steve Morrison, Juliane K. Munson, Elizabeth B. Rasmussen, Ellen Sadler, Rachael L. Shaw, Sivan B. Sherman, Diane Auger Smith, Laura Tortorelli, Khara Turnbull, Miriam E. Vidaver, Michelle L. Warner, Catherine S. Whittington, Jeannette A. Williams

We would like to extend special recognition to Program Directors Matthew Davis and Souzanne Wright who were instrumental to the early development of this program.

Schools

We are truly grateful to the teachers, students, and administrators of the following schools for their willingness to field test these materials and for their invaluable advice: Capitol View Elementary, Challenge Foundation Academy (IN), Community Academy Public Charter School, Lake Lure Classical Academy, Lepanto Elementary School, New Holland Core Knowledge Academy, Paramount School of Excellence, Pioneer Challenge Foundation Academy, New York City PS 26R (The Carteret School), PS 30X (Wilton School), PS 50X (Clara Barton School), PS 96Q, PS 102X (Joseph O. Loretan), PS 104Q (The Bays Water), PS 214K (Michael Friedsam), PS 223Q (Lyndon B. Johnson School), PS 308K (Clara Cardwell), PS 333Q (Goldie Maple Academy), Sequoyah Elementary School, South Shore Charter Public School, Spartanburg Charter School, Steed Elementary School, Thomas Jefferson Classical Academy, Three Oaks Elementary, West Manor Elementary.

And a special thanks to the CKLA Pilot Coordinators Anita Henderson, Yasmin Lugo-Hernandez, and Susan Smith, whose suggestions and day-to-day support to teachers using these materials in their classrooms was critical.

Core Knowledge Language Arts

Core Knowledge®

Editorial Staff

Susan Lambert, Vice President, CKLA
Rachel Wolf, Editorial Director
Sarah McClurg, Senior Content Specialist
Elizabeth Wade, PhD, Managing Curriculum Developer
Patricia Erno, Senior Curriculum Developer
Jamie Raade, Senior Curriculum Developer
Marc Goldsmith, Curriculum Developer
Carrie Hughes, Curriculum Developer
Amber McWilliams, ELL Specialist
Brian Black, Managing Copy Editor

Project Management

Matthew Ely, Senior Project Manager
Jennifer Skelley, Senior Producer
Cesar Parra, Project Manager

Design and Graphics Staff

Todd Rawson, Design Director
Chris O'Flaherty, Art Director
Carmela Stricklett, Art Director
Stephanie Cooper, Art Director
Annah Kessler, Visual Designer
Erin O'Donnell, Senior Production Designer
Tim Chi Ly, Illustrator
John Starr, Illustrator

Contributors

Ann Andrew
Desirée Beach
Leslie Beach
Nicole Crook
Stephen Currie
Kira Dykema
Carol Emerson
Jennifer Flewelling
Mairin Genova
Christina Gonzalez Vega
Stephanie Hamilton
Rowena Hymer
Brooke Hudson
Jason Jacobs
Leslie Johnson
Debra Levitt
Bridget Looney
Christina Martinez
Julie McGeorge
Evelyn Norman
Leighann Pennington
Heather Perry
Tim Quiroz
Maureen Richel
Jessica Richardson
Carol Ronka
Laura Seal
Cynthia Shields
Alison Tepper
Karen Venditti
Carri Waloven
Michelle Warner

Writers

Matt Davis

Illustrators and Image Sources

All illustrations by Jed Henry

Credits

Every effort has been taken to trace and acknowledge copyrights. The editors tender their apologies for any accidental infringement where copyright has proved untraceable. They would be pleased to insert the appropriate acknowledgment in any subsequent edition of this publication. Trademarks and trade names are shown in this publication for illustrative purposes only and are the property of their respective owners. The references to trademarks and trade names given herein do not affect their validity.

All photographs are used under license from Shutterstock, Inc. unless otherwise noted.